ScottForesman

D'Nealian® Handwriting

Third Edition

Book **5**

Author
Donald Neal Thurber

 ScottForesman

A Division of HarperCollins*Publishers*

Editorial Offices: Glenview, Illinois
Regional Offices: Sunnyvale, California • Tucker, Georgia
Glenview, Illinois • Oakland, New Jersey • Dallas, Texas

Acknowledgments

Text
page 22: Barbara J. Winston et al., *Geography: Our Country and Our World*, Grade 4. Glenview: Scott, Foresman and Company, 1991 page 274.
page 23: From *Class President* by Johanna Hurwitz. Text copyright © 1990 by Johanna Hurwitz. Illustrations copyright © 1990 by Sheila Hamanaka. Reprinted by permission of William Morrow & Company, Inc./Publishers, New York.
page 45: From *One Day in the Tropical Rain Forest* by Jean Craighead George. Text copyright © 1990 by Jean Craighead George. Selection reprinted by permission of HarperCollins Publishers and Curtis Brown Ltd.
page 57: From *The Long Winter* by Laura Ingalls Wilder. Text copyright 1940 by Laura Ingalls Wilder, renewed © 1968 by Roger L. MacBride. Illustrations coypright 1953 by Garth WIlliams, renewed © 1981 by Garth Williams. Selection reprinted by permission of HarperCollins Publishers and Lutterworth Press.
page 74: From ''About Notebooks'' in *Hey World, Here I Am!* by Jean Little. Text copyright © 1986 by Jean Little. Selection reprinted by permission of HarperCollins Publishers and Kids Can Press Ltd.
page 85: Reprinted by permission of Sterling Publishing Co., Inc., 387 Park Avenue South, New York, NY 10016 from *The Zaniest Riddle Book in the World* by Joseph Rosenbloom, © 1984 by Joseph Rosenbloom.
page 88: ''The Falling Star'' by Sara Teasdale. Reprinted with permission of Macmillan Publishing Company from *Collected Poems* by Sara Teasdale. Copyright 1930 by Sara Teasdale Filsinger, renewed 1958 by Guaranty Trust Co. of N.Y.
page 89: ''On the Beach'' by Dorothy Aldis. Reprinted by permission of G.P. Putnam's Sons from *Hello Day* by Dorothy Aldis, copyright © 1959 by Dorothy Aldis, copyright renewed © 1987 by Roy E. Porter.
page 93: From *Justin and the Best Biscuits in the World* by Mildred Pitts Walter with illustrations by Catherine Stock. Text copyright © 1986 by Mildred Pitts Walter. Illustrations copyright © 1986 by Catherine Stock. Reprinted by permission of William Morrow & Company, Inc./Publishers, New York.

Illustrations
Rondi Collette 36; Laura D'Argo 72; Nancy Didion 84 (bottom); Malcolm Farley 45; Linda Hawkins 84 (top); Gary Hoover 6, 38, 85; Richard Kreigler 8, 18; Judith Love 49; Yoshi Miyaki 60, 75, 76; Deb Morse 7, 69; James Needham 31; Kate Pagni (calligraphy) 70, 71; Anna Rich 93; Judy Sakaguchi 32, 33; Cindy Salans-Rosenheim 89; Bob Shein 9, 44, 91; Georgia Shola 12, 42, 80, 92; Stephen Snodgrass 23; Ken Spiering 50; Krystina Stasiak 17, 88; Carol Stutz (lettering) 16, 18, 19, 24, 30, 40, 46, 52, 58, 73, 94; Susan Swan 43, 68; Andrea Tachiera 70, 71; Darcy Whitehead 3, 4, 5, 11, 12, 16, 17, 22, 23, 26, 28, 61, 69, 81

Photographs
H. Armstrong Roberts/J. Irwin 21; H. Armstrong Roberts/G. Aherns 22; H. Armstrong Roberts 49 (left); Image Bank/Charles S. Allen 53 (top); Image Bank/Don Klumpp 56; Tom Stack/Allen B. Smith 54; Tom Stack/John Cancalosi 55 (left); Tony Stone Worldwide/Sandy King 49 (right); Superstock, Inc. 55 (right)

Staff Credits
Editorial: Marianne Hiland, Gerry Murphy-Ferguson, Delores Nemo, and Bridget McCarron
Design: Paula Meyers
Production: Barbara Albright and Maryann Lewis
Marketing: Sue Cowden and Kristine Stanczak

D'Nealian® Handwriting is a registered trademark of Donald Neal Thurber.

Contents

Unit One

Reviewing Manuscript Letters

Reviewing Lower-case Manuscript Letters

Write a row of each lower-case letter.

a

b

c

d

e

f

g

h

i

j

k

l

m

n

o

p

q

r

s

t

u

v

w

x

y

z

WILD
IDEAS

Write the phrases in manuscript.

zebras with wings

jiffy kite

words that move

oxen dancers

purple quarters

Reviewing Capital Manuscript Letters

Write a row of each capital letter.

A   J   S

B   K   T

C   L   U

D   M   V

E   N   W

F   O   X

G   P   Y

H   Q   Z

I   R

Some famous authors have written books of fantasy. Write these authors' names in manuscript.

Rumer Godden

Ursula K. Le Guin

Carl Sandburg

James Thurber

Reviewing Numbers

Write a row of each number.

1 _____   6 _____

2 _____   7 _____

3 _____   8 _____

4 _____   9 _____

5 _____   10 _____

When you write a number that has more than three digits, use a comma to separate the hundreds column from the thousands column. Look at the examples in the chart at the right.

Imagine that you are a space explorer of the future. You keep a log that gives information about your trips.

Write some imaginary numbers that tell how many of each item below you have heard or seen. Use big numbers, like those in the chart.

hundred-thousands	ten-thousands	thousands	hundreds	tens	ones
2	6	3,5	0	1	
	4	7,2	8	9	
		1,7	3	6	

waterfalls on Jupiter   _____

new command centers   _____

valleys on the moon   _____

comets you saw today   _____

signals from Neptune   _____

space cities   _____

shuttle deliveries   _____

8

Writing a Postcard

Most postcards have limited space for writing. When you send someone a postcard, you need to adjust your handwriting to fit the space.

Notice how LaTrice fit her handwriting on the postcard below. She wrote smaller than usual, but her writing is still neat and easy to read.

MAY 17, 199_

Dear Mindy,

    I'm at my grandmother's in Michigan. She has a beautiful flower garden. I'm going to help her plant a tree today. See you next Friday.

        Love,
        LaTrice

MINDY JACKSON
4815 W VAN BUREN
CHICAGO IL 60644

Copy LaTrice's postcard, or write one of your own in the space below. Adjust your handwriting to fit the space. Write in manuscript. For the address, use all capital letters and no punctuation marks.

Writing an Invitation

Here's a challenge. Write smaller than you usually do and keep your writing legible at the same time.

Read Vaughn's invitation. Then copy it in manuscript in the smaller space below. Notice that you have more lines, but they are shorter. Before you begin, plan how you will adjust your handwriting to fit the space.

June 4, 199___

Dear Anthony,
Please come to my birthday party on June 28. It will start around 2:00. My aunt will drive us to the pool. We will have a picnic afterward.
Your friend,
Vaughn

Unit Two

Writing Cursive Letters

Writing Cursive lL, hH, and kK

Write a row of each lower-case letter. Be sure to
- touch the top line with the uphill stroke.
- write **l, h,** and **k** with loops.

Notice where the capital letters **L, H,** and **K** touch the top line. Write a row of each letter.

Capital Letter Link-ups
Remember that **L** and **K** join the letters that follow them. Trace the joined letters in the box.

H does not join the letter that follows it. Trace **He.**

Li Ka
He

Write the following names of imaginary places.

Klick Klack Headquarters

Hilly Lily Lighthouse

Writing Cursive tT, iI, and uU

Write a row of each lower-case letter. Be sure to
- make **u** half as tall as **t.**
- cross **t** and dot **i.**

Notice where the capital letters **T, I,** and **U** touch the top line. Write a row of each letter.

Capital Letter Link-ups

Remember that **I** and **U** join the letters that follow them. Trace the joined letters in the box.

T does not join the letter that follows it. Trace **Tr.**

In Us

Tr

Write the following imaginary signs.

Invisible Truck Users

Investigators of Traveling Ushers

13

Writing Cursive eE, jJ, and pP

Write a row of each lower-case letter. Be sure to
- keep **e** open.
- write **j** with a loop and **p** without a loop.

Notice where the capital letters **E, J,** and **P** touch the top line. Write a row of each letter.

Capital Letter Link-ups

Remember that **E** and **J** join the letters that follow them. Trace the joined letters in the box.

P does not join the letter that follows it. Trace **Pa.**

Es   Ju
Pa

Write the following travel slogans about imaginary trips.

Escape to Jukebox Paradise

Enjoy a Journey to Parjanap

Practice

Some letter combinations appear more often than others.
Write a row of each pair of letters. Be sure to
- make tall letters touch the top line.
- write **h** and **k** with loops.

sh   *sh*

th   *th*

ck   *ck*

Now write the following names and the sentences below.
Be sure to write **h** and **k** correctly.

Jack Frost   *Misha Perth*

Jules loaned Lakesha a thick book on talking pets.

She said she would bring it back.

Her brothers Mick and Seth thought they should read it too.

The pets lived in three shacks.

Review

Remember that you join capital letters **L, K, I, U, E,** and **J** to the lower-case letters that follow them. Write the following names.

Lucia

_____

Kimiko

_____

Ignacio

_____

Ugo

_____

Ethel

_____

Jetty

_____

Remember that you do not join capital letters **P, T,** and **H** to the lower-case letters that follow them. Write these names of imaginary places.

Puck Island

_____

Top Town

_____

Harsylvania

_____

Spot a Problem

Tell why the cursive words below are hard to read.

track

track

_____

high

high

_____

Now write the words so that they will be easy to read.

_____

_____

Write the following phrase. Make sure you write **h** and **k** correctly.

through a fabulous kingdom

_____

_____

Evaluation

Read the hints. Then write the paragraph below. Make your handwriting easy to read.

Hints for Clear Handwriting
- Make your tall letters touch the top line.
- Make your small letters half the size of your tall letters.

   I put on my magic cape. Filled with hope, I started up a rough path through the dark forest. The moon was rising. It was eight o'clock. Near the hilltop, I waited for Piku. A long journey lay ahead of us.

_____

_____

_____

_____

_____

_____

Check Your Handwriting

Is your handwriting improving? Use the marks below to check the paragraph you wrote.

In the second sentence, **circle** tall letters that do not touch the top line.

In the third sentence, **write a check mark above** small letters that are too tall.

On the lines below, write the number of marks you made.

○ _____   √ _____

Low scores mean your handwriting is easy to read!

Is Your Writing Legible?

Is your writing easy to read, or is it a mystery? Maybe sometimes even you can't read it. Make sure that every letter you write is clear and legible. Check for the following points in your handwriting.

Letter Size and Proportion

Your writing will be legible if your letters are the correct size. Make your small letters half the size of your tall letters. Make your tall letters touch the top line. Make your descenders go below the bottom line.

Using four or five of the letters on the right, make up a funny name for yourself. Write it below. Remember to capitalize the first letter. Keep all your letters the correct size and proportion.

Letter Form

Your writing will be easy to read if you form your letters correctly. Can you read the word at the right? The word is **ideas.** What makes it hard to read?

Write **ideas** legibly. Remember to dot **i,** make **d** touch the top line, and keep the loop open on **e.** Close **a** and **s.**

Write the phrase below in cursive. Concentrate on forming your letters correctly.

flights of fancy

Ask a classmate to read the phrase you wrote. Does he or she think it is legible?

Letter Slant

Your writing will be easy to read if you slant all your letters in the same direction. Once you know what the natural slant of your own writing is, keep it the same.

Pretend it is the year 1999. You live on a star, and you go to Dream High School. Write the name of your future school.

_____

_____

Look at the words you wrote. Then look at the examples below. Write the description of your slant.

right   *left*   *up and down*

Letter and Word Spacing

Make your writing legible by having the right amount of spacing between letters and words. Don't crowd letters too closely together. Leave more space between words than between letters in a word.

Write the sentence below.

Imagine the future!

_____

_____

Look at the examples below. Then look at the sentence you wrote. Write the word or words that describe the spacing in your handwriting.

even   *too close*

too far apart

Using Proofreading Marks

The proofreading marks in the paragraph below indicate changes that the writer wants to make. Check the list at the right to see what the marks mean.

¶ Hank Aaron holds the
sp record
major-league rekord for
home runs—755⊙ and
        also
he∧ holds the record for
runs batted in—2,297!

Rewrite the paragraph, making the changes. You do not need to skip any lines.

Look at what you wrote. Did you make each correction indicated? Do your letters all slant in the same direction?

Read the paragraph below. Notice the mistakes. Use the proofreading marks on page 20 to show how the mistakes should be corrected.

In 1899 Nellie bly went around the world in 72 days, 6 hours, 11 minutes in those those days nobdy thogt it could be done

Now rewrite the paragraph, making the corrections.

Timed Writing

Domingo was studying for a test in geography. He had to finish in time for his next class. He realized that he would have to write quickly to make notes from the following paragraph.

The most powerful shapers of the western landscape are rivers. Most rivers of the West begin in the Rocky Mountains. Some of these flow west toward the Pacific Ocean. Others flow east toward the Great Plains. An imaginary line called the Continental Divide runs north and south along the top of the Rockies. This line separates the rivers that flow west from those that flow east. Use the map on page 272 to find the Continental Divide.

When you have to write quickly, use these tips.
- First, read what you have to copy. Think about how you can write it in a shorter form and still get all the important information.
- Use manuscript or cursive, whichever you write faster.
- Write only important words and phrases.

Now write notes from the paragraph above. Time your writing. Use a clock, a timer, or have someone time you. Stop writing when four minutes are up.

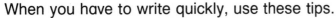

Now read what you have written. Is your writing easy to read? Did you include only important words and phrases?

Reading and Writing

In the book *Class President* by Johanna Hurwitz, the principal of Julio's school has said that there is to be no soccer-playing at recess. Julio goes with two classmates to see the principal.

Read these paragraphs from the story to find out how Julio used his imagination to convince the principal to change his mind.

Julio took a deep breath. If Cricket or Lucas wasn't going to talk, he would have to do it. Julio started right in.

"We came to tell you that it isn't fair that no one can play soccer at recess just because Arthur Lewis broke his eyeglasses. Anybody can have an accident. He could have tripped and broken them getting on the school bus." Julio was amazed that so many words had managed to get out of his mouth. No one else said anything, so he went on. "Besides, a girl could fall jumping rope," said Julio. "But you didn't say that they had to stop jumping rope."

"I hadn't thought of that," said Mr. Herbertson. Cricket looked alarmed. "Can't we jump rope anymore?" she asked.

"I didn't mean that you should make the girls stop jumping rope," Julio went on quickly. He stopped to think of a better example. "Your chair could break while you're sitting on it, Mr. Herbertson," he said.

Mr. Herbertson adjusted himself in his chair. "I certainly hope not," he said, smiling. ■

Think of a situation in which you might want to convince someone to agree with your point of view. After you choose a topic, write it below. Then write a list of arguments you could use. Here are some possible topics: the need for recycling; the most interesting hobby; the best athlete; the greatest president; why we should use our imaginations.

_____

_____

_____

_____

_____

_____

_____

Joel wrote about persuading his classmates to elect him president. Read the sentences he wrote to start.

> I have good ideas about improving our class spirit. I am not afraid to give my opinions. We should have more projects. I would listen to your complaints.

Read what Joel wrote.

	Yes	No
• Did he tell what arguments he would use?	☐	☐
• Did he state his topic clearly?	☐	☐

Proofread Joel's sentences.

	Yes	No
• Are his small letters half the size of his tall letters?	☐	☐
• Do his tall letters touch the top line?	☐	☐

Copy Joel's sentences on a sheet of paper. Be sure to make small letters half the size of tall letters. Make tall letters touch the top line.

Write a composition about the topic you chose on page 24. Use arguments to convince someone to agree with your point of view. You may want to use some of the ideas from your list.

_____

_____

_____

_____

_____

_____

_____

_____

_____

_____

_____

_____

_____

_____

_____

_____

Read your draft carefully.   Yes   No
- Did you tell what arguments you would use?   ☐   ☐
- Did you state your topic clearly?   ☐   ☐

Proofread your work.
- Are your small letters half the size of your tall letters?   ☐   ☐
- Do your tall letters touch the top line?   ☐   ☐

Edit your copy. Can you make it more convincing by adding stronger arguments? If so, include them. Then write the revised copy on another sheet of paper.

Writing Cursive aA, dD, and cC

Write a row of each lower-case letter. Be sure to
- close **a** and **d.**
- keep **c** open.

Notice where the capital letters **A, D,** and **C** touch the top line. Write a row of each letter.

Capital Letter Link-ups

Remember that **A** and **C** join the letters that follow them. Trace the joined letters in the box.

D does not join the letter that follows it. Trace **De.**

> *At Co*
>
> *De*

Write the following names of places.

Atlantic Ocean   *Alps*

Painted Desert   *Coast Range*

Writing Cursive nN, mM, and xX

Imagine that there is a midline on the lines below. Write a row of each lower-case letter. Make **n, m,** and **x** touch the imaginary midline.

Notice that capital letters **N, M,** and **X** have the same beginning stroke. Write a row of each letter.

 Capital Letter Link-ups
Remember that **N** and **M** join the letters that follow them. Trace the joined letters in the box.

X does not join the letter that follows it. Trace **Xo.**

Na Me
Xo

Write the following names of places.

Nanjing

Miami Beach

Xuzhou

New Mexico

Writing Cursive gG, yY, and qQ

Write a row of each lower-case letter. Be sure to
- swing the bottom loops of **g** and **y** to the left.
- swing the bottom loop of **q** to the right.

Notice that capital letters **Q** and **Y** start near the top line.
G starts at the bottom line. Write a row of each letter.

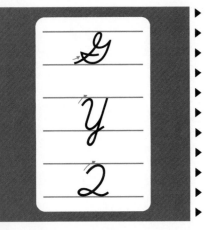

Capital Letter Link-ups
Remember that **Y** and **Q** join the letters that follow them.
Trace the joined letters in the box.

G does not join the letter that follows it. Trace **Gr.**

Write the following names of places.

Yellow Sea   *Qiqihar*

Galway Bay   *Yugoslavia*

Practice

Some letter combinations appear more often than others.
Write a row of each pair of letters. Be sure to
- swing the loop on **y** to the left.
- close **a.**
- cross **t.**

na   *na*

ty   *ty*

Now write the following names and the sentences below.
Be sure to open **y**, close **a**, and cross **t.**

Canada   *Bay City*

We can learn to respect the
beauty of our land.

Our national parks preserve it.

It is our duty to manage the
use of natural resources wisely.

One type of activity is to stop
pollution in a city or town.

29

Review

Remember that you join capital letters **A, C, N, M, Y,** and **Q** to the lower-case letters that follow them. Write these names.

Akemi

_____

Cynthia

_____

Nadine

_____

Marcus

_____

Yancy

_____

Quincy

_____

Remember that you do not join capital letters **D, X,** and **G** to the lower-case letters that follow them. Write these names of places.

Delhi

_____

Xiamen

_____

Great Falls

_____

Spot a Problem

Tell why the cursive words below are hard to read.

sequoia

sequoia

animal

aninae

Now write **sequoia** and **animal** so that they will be easy to read.

_____

_____

Write the following phrase. Make sure your closed letters are properly formed.

migrant geese in coastal waters

_____

_____

Evaluation

Read the hints. Then write the paragraph below. Make your handwriting easy to read.

Hints for Clear Handwriting
- Use only cursive letters.
- Keep **y** open at the top.

Nature is full of wonder. The more closely we watch, the better we will understand it. You can see nature's beauty everywhere, in the sky, in trees, in birds and animals. All you have to do is look around.

Check Your Handwriting

Is your handwriting improving? Use the marks below to check the paragraph you wrote.

In the first sentence, **circle every** letter that is not in cursive.

In the third sentence, **write a check mark above every y** that is not open at the top.

On the lines below, write the number of marks you made.

◯ _____   √ _____

Low scores mean your handwriting is easy to read!

Letter Size and Proportion

Remember that your writing will be easy to read if you make each letter the correct size. The lower-case letters of the alphabet are grouped below by size. Notice that **f** is both a tall and a descender letter.

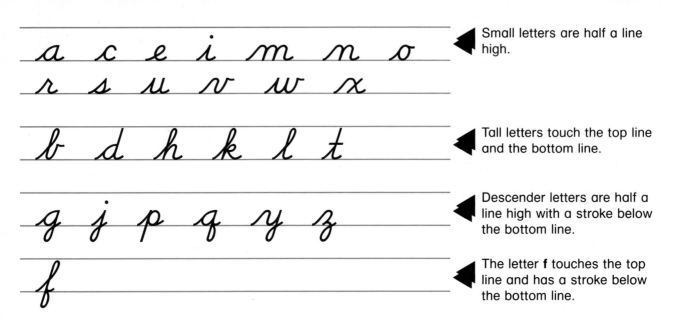

Small letters are half a line high.

Tall letters touch the top line and the bottom line.

Descender letters are half a line high with a stroke below the bottom line.

The letter **f** touches the top line and has a stroke below the bottom line.

Copy the following paragraph in cursive. Think about the size of each letter as you write.

Have you ever written a message in the sand or picked up a soft stone to draw a picture on the sidewalk? If so, you were using natural resources as tools.

Look at the paragraph you just wrote. Are you satisfied with the size of each letter?

Sometimes you may have to adjust the spacing of your letters as you write so that your tall letters don't "bump" into your descender letters. Make sure your writing doesn't look like the writing in the sentence below.

Our supply of natural resources will be used quickly.

Now write the sentence above. Adjust the spacing if you need to keep letters from bumping into each other. Be careful not to change the size of your small, tall, and descender letters.

It is not always necessary for your tall letters to touch the top line when you write. Sometimes you may want to use **adult proportion.** This means that your capital and tall letters do not touch the top line, but your small letters are still in proportion to them. The sentences below are written in adult proportion.

The United States has a rich supply of natural resources. One is vegetation, such as grass.

Now copy the sentences above, using adult proportion. Remember to make your small letters half as high as your tall letters.

Filling Out a Form

When you fill out a form, you must often adjust your handwriting to fit a small space. Before writing, notice how much space is allowed.

Rachel wanted to order some catalogs. She filled out the form below. Notice the instruction <u>Please print.</u> This means to write in manuscript. When you have to write small, manuscript is often easier to use.

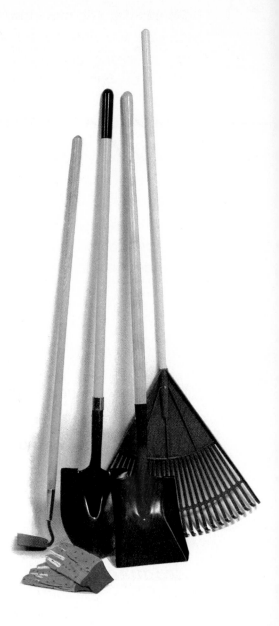

Send me catalogs on the following:

✔ Camping Equipment ✔ Work Clothes and Tools

_____ Gardening ✔ Sporting Goods

Other information (Please specify.) *A catalog on games*

_____

Mail the information to: (Please print.)

Name *Rachel Grey Eagle*

Street *1220 Settler Way*

City *Beaverton* State *Oregon* ZIP *97005*

Use your name and address to fill out the form. For <u>Other Information</u>, specify the type of catalog you want. Write in manuscript.

Send me catalogs on the following:

_____ Camping Equipment _____ Work Clothes and Tools

_____ Gardening _____ Sporting Goods

Other information (Please specify.)

_____

Mail the information to: (Please print.)

Name

Street

City State ZIP

Addressing an Envelope

When you write addresses on an envelope, you need to
write smaller than you usually do. Look at the envelope
below. Notice the return address and the mailing address.

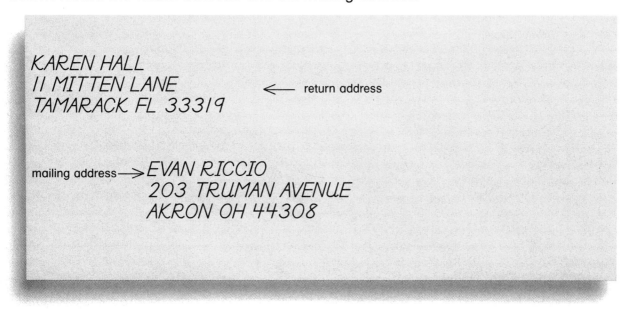

KAREN HALL
11 MITTEN LANE   ← return address
TAMARACK FL 33319

mailing address → EVAN RICCIO
                  203 TRUMAN AVENUE
                  AKRON OH 44308

On the envelope below, copy the addresses, or write two
others. Adjust your writing to fit the space. You will not need
to use punctuation for any abbreviations. Write all capital
letters in manuscript. Remember to keep your writing
straight, even though there are no writing lines.

Fun with Handwriting: Business Cards

Adults often ask you, "What are you going to be when you grow up?" Have you decided on your future career? It's fun to think about. Sara and some of her friends discussed the future one day. They decided to make their own business cards. Read the cards below.

Sara Greenberg and Company
Perfection Party Planners
Sara Greenberg
President
Dot Lake
Alaska

Montez Motors, Inc.
800 Ruth Court
Sacramento CA 95823
Alberto Montez
Chief Engineer

The Outer Limits
Planet-to-Planet Travel
Greg Holt, Head Agent
Box 1000, Tower X33, Mars

LAWNS UNLIMITED
Landscaping to Order
Lucy Payo, Crew Manager
Santiago, Spain

Copy one of the business cards in the space below, or create a card for yourself. Write neatly in cursive or manuscript.

If you want to make other business cards for yourself, write them on plain index cards. Then share them with your family and friends.

Writing Cursive oO, wW, and bB

Write a row of each lower-case letter. Be sure to
- close **o.**
- keep the loop open on **b.**

Notice that capital letters **O** and **B** start at the top line. **W** starts just below the top line. Write a row of each letter.

 Capital Letter Link-ups
Remember that **O, W,** and **B** do not join the letters that follow them. Trace the letter combinations in the box.

Or Wa
Bl

Write the following names of places.

Oregon Trail   *Botswana*

Wabash River   *Blue Ridge*

Joining Sidestroke Letters

Look at letters **o** and **n** at the right. Now look at the joined letters in **on.** Notice that
- before joining, the beginning stroke of **n** touches the bottom line.
- after joining, the beginning stroke of **n** does not touch the bottom line.

o n on

When you join the letters **o, w,** and **b** to other letters, do not touch the bottom line.

on   wh   br

Write the words and sentences below.

bobcat   weasel   wolf

ocelot   beetle   owl

*We woke before noon and walked
to the wilderness area.*

*I saw a bear and her cubs, a
beaver, and a big raccoon.*

38

Practice

Some letter combinations appear more often than others.
Write a row of each pair of letters. Be sure to
- keep the loop open on **b**.
- close **o**.
- make **o** and **w** half as tall as **b**.

bo   *bo*

or   *or*

wi   *wi*

Now write the following names and the sentences below.
Be sure to keep the loop open on **b** and close **o**.

Bar Harbor   *North Sea*

The wide gorge is a refuge for plants and wildlife.

Bob has a boat nearby.

From here you can see the widest part of the bottom of the canyon.

Review

Remember that you do not join capital cursive letters **O**, **W**, and **B** to the lower-case letters that follow them. Write these names.

Bebe
_____

_____

Owen
_____

_____

Wotanda
_____

_____

Wilbert
_____

_____

Bo
_____

_____

Ora
_____

_____

Remember to make your small letters half as tall as your tall letters. Write these names of places.

Oceanside
_____

_____

Wyoming
_____

_____

Baltic Sea
_____

_____

Spot a Problem

Tell why the cursive words below are hard to read.

soil

soil
_____

_____

water

Water
_____

_____

Now write **soil** and **water** so that they will be easy to read.
_____

_____

Write the following phrase. Use a sidestroke to join **o, w,** and **b** to lower-case letters that follow them.

boots for walking on trails
_____

_____

40

Evaluation

Read the hints. Then write the paragraph below. Make your handwriting easy to read.

Hints for Clear Handwriting
- Close **o.**
- Write **b** with a loop.

Toby drew a picture of boats in a harbor. Most of them were brown. One had a wide white sail. He used orange and blue for the sunset. The border was purple and black.

_____

_____

_____

_____

_____

_____

 Check Your Handwriting

Is your handwriting improving? Use the marks below to check the paragraph you wrote.

In the first sentence, **circle** every **b** that does not have a loop.

In the second sentence, **write a check mark above** every **o** that is not closed.

On the lines below, write the number of marks you made.

◯ _____   √ _____

Low scores mean your handwriting is easy to read!

Letter Form

Your writing will be easy to read if you form your letters correctly. Remember these rules.

- Join **o, w, b,** and **v** to the letters that follow with a sidestroke.
- Close **a** and **o.**
- Cross **t** and dot **i** and **j.**
- Write **b, h, k,** and **l** with a loop.
- Write **d, i, p,** and **t** without a loop.
- The letters **f** and **z** have descenders.

Write the following sentences.

Good soil may be destroyed by erosion.

Erosion is the wearing away of soil by wind, water, or ice.

Farmers have ways of preventing erosion.

One method is to plow back and forth across a hill instead of up and down.

Read the paragraph below. Then copy it. As you write, concentrate on forming each letter correctly. Remember to follow the rules on page 42. Don't let your tall letters bump into your descenders.

Environment is everything that surrounds us. Forests, rivers, mountains, and fields are all part of it. In the late 1960s, people realized that the environment was slowly being destroyed. Air and water were polluted. Waste was dumped into lakes and rivers. Too many trees were being cut down. Today we know that we must protect our environment.

Timed Writing

Sumi was waiting for a commercial on TV about a street fair in her neighborhood. When the information flashed on the screen, she wrote it as rapidly as she could. Read the commercial below.

Oak River Street Fair

All day Saturday, September 24 10:00 a.m. till 5:00 p.m.

Face-painting, arts and crafts, mimes, food!

Kids, have your photo taken in Caron Park, 1–4 p.m.

All the action is on Harris Street between Lin and James Avenues.

When you must write something quickly, use these tips.
- Write in manuscript or cursive, whichever you can do faster.
- Write only important information.
- Write legibly even though you are writing fast.

Write the information you need from the commercial. Time your writing. Use a clock, a timer, or ask someone to time you. Stop writing when four minutes are up.

_____

_____

_____

_____

_____

Read your notes on the commercial. Did you write only important information? Is your writing legible?

Reading and Writing

One Day in the Tropical Rain Forest is a book by Jean Craighead George. The story is about Tepui, an Indian boy in Venezuela, who helps a scientist trying to save the rain forest from destruction. The author describes in detail the plant and animal life of the jungle.

Read the following excerpt from the book. Notice how closely the author has observed the activities of a macaw—a large parrot.

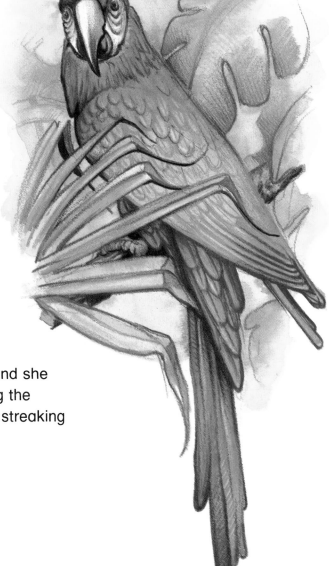

A scarlet macaw hooked her beak on a vine and pulled herself abreast of her last year's nest. She looked into a dark deep hole in the tallest tree in the Tropical Rain Forest of the Macaw. Spring was coming, and it was time to clean her nest. The big parrot was mostly red. Her lower back and outer tail feathers were bright blue. Yellow feathers tipped with green gleamed on her wings. She opened them. They spread three feet from tip to tip. When she flew, she looked like a fiery meteor. Below her a flock of orange-winged parrots began to chatter. A pair of blue and green parakeets touched beaks in a bower of silver webbing. It had been spun during the night by a busy spider. Like the millions of other webs draped through the forest, this one sparkled with raindrops.

The mate of the scarlet macaw called to her, and she joined him on the flight to the cashew trees along the Orinoco River. Thirty other macaws joined them, streaking the sky red as they flew off to eat. ■

Think about something beautiful you have seen. It might be a bird, an animal, a flower, or even a natural scene such as a mountain range or a forest. Write some words in the Word Bank below that you could use to describe your topic.

Word Bank

_____   _____

_____   _____

_____   _____

_____   _____

Carthel wrote a description of a lake on a warm, sunny day. Read his sentences below.

The water is smooth and shiny. Waves are rolling in slowly. They sound very calm as they ripple on the sand. They make it look like glass.

Read what Carthel wrote.

	Yes	No
• Did he write descriptive details?	☐	☐
• Can you picture the lake in your mind?	☐	☐

Proofread Carthel's sentences.

	Yes	No
• Are the letters formed correctly?	☐	☐
• Did Carthel adjust his writing so that his tall letters don't bump into letters with descenders?	☐	☐

On a sheet of paper, copy Carthel's sentences. Form all the letters correctly. Adjust your writing so that your tall letters don't bump into letters with descenders.

Write about something beautiful that you have seen. Use some of the descriptive details you wrote in your Word Bank on page 46.

_____

_____

_____

_____

_____

_____

_____

_____

_____

_____

_____

_____

_____

Read your draft carefully.   Yes   No
- Did you write descriptive details?   ☐   ☐
- Can you picture what you wrote about in your mind?   ☐   ☐

Proofread your work.
- Are your letters formed correctly?   ☐   ☐
- Did you adjust your writing so that your tall letters don't bump into letters with descenders?   ☐   ☐

Make changes to improve your draft. Can you add more descriptive details? Write your neat final copy on another sheet of paper.

Writing Cursive vV and zZ

Imagine that there is a midline on the lines below. Write a
row of each lower-case letter. Make **v** and **z** touch the
imaginary midline.

Notice that capital letters **V** and **Z** start near the top line.
Write a row of each letter.

 Capital Letter Link-ups
Remember that **Z** joins the letter that follows it.
Trace the joined letters in the box.

V does not join the letter that follows it. Trace **Vi.**

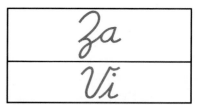

Write the following phrases.

from Vietnam to Zanesville

from Zimbabwe to Valdez

Zanzibar in Tanzania

Writing Cursive sS, rR, and fF

Write a row of each lower-case letter. Be sure to
- keep **r** open.
- close **s.**

s   *s*

r   *r*

f   *f*

Notice that capital **F** has three strokes. Write a row of each letter.

S   *S*

R   *R*

F   *F*

Capital Letter Link-ups

Remember that **R** joins the letter that follows it. Trace the joined letters in the box.

S and **F** do not join the letters that follow them. Trace **St** and **Fa.**

Re
St Fa

Write the following phrases.

Family Traditions

Stories of Reunion

Joining Sidestroke Letters

Look at letters **o, w, b,** and **v** at the right. They end with sidestrokes. These strokes do not touch the bottom line.

o   w   b   v

Use a sidestroke when you join **o, w, b,** and **v** to other letters.

of   wr   bu   ve

Write the words and sentences below.

better   *went*   *vast*

view   *off*   *out*

An ocean voyage was part of the immigrants' experience.

Some got jobs cutting lumber or working in factories.

Practice

Some letter combinations appear more often than others.
Write a row of each pair of letters. Be sure to

- close **s.**
- join **v** to other letters with a sidestroke.

sa   *sa*

ve   *ve*

Now write the following names and the sentences below.
Be sure to close **s** and join **v** to other letters with a
sidestroke.

Rosa Vilan   *Felipe Chavez*

We live in different places.

We preserve distinctive customs.

*I say we must share the same
liberty in order to save it.*

*Whoever wants a safe future
salutes the rights of everyone.*

Review

Remember that you join capital letters **Z** and **R** to the lower-case letters that follow them. Write these names.

Zia

Rod

Rena

Riki

Zhenya

Zoe

Remember that you do not join capital letters **V, S,** and **F** to the lower-case letters that follow them. Write the names of these places.

Vienna

Senegal

Finland

Spot a Problem

Tell why the cursive words below are hard to read.

rich

rich

variety

variety

Now write **rich** and **variety** so that they will be easy to read.

Write the following phrase. Make sure your small letters are half the size of your tall letters.

citizens from different countries

52

Evaluation

Read the hints. Then write the paragraph below. Make your handwriting easy to read.

Hints for Clear Handwriting
- Keep the loops open on **f.**
- Close **s.**

We Americans have a rich cultural background. Because we are of different races, we follow a variety of customs. Some of us were born in the United States, while others came from many different countries.

Check Your Handwriting

Is your handwriting improving? Use the marks below to check the paragraph you wrote.

In the second sentence, **circle** every **f** that does not have an open loop.

In the third sentence, **write a check mark above** every **s** that is not closed.

On the lines below, write the number of marks you made.

○ _____   √ _____

Low scores mean your handwriting is easy to read!

Letter Slant

You can help make your handwriting legible by always slanting it in the same direction. Use the slant that is natural for you, whether it is right, left, or straight up and down.

Answer the following question by copying one of the sentences below.

In which direction does your handwriting slant?
My handwriting slants to the right.
My handwriting slants to the left.
My handwriting is straight up and down.

Write the sentences below. Use the same slant for letters, punctuation marks, and numbers.

Of the 50 United States, 26 have names that come from Indian words.

Iowa means "beautiful land."

What does your state's name mean?

Have fun finding out!

Read the paragraph below.

Who were the first settlers of North America? They were Indians from Asia. They arrived more than 30,000 years ago! Europeans came much later, around A.D. 1500. Each group of Indians had different types of homes, food, clothing, and customs. The Indians' way of life is called their culture.

Now copy the paragraph. Remember to slant all your letters in the same direction. Be sure that punctuation marks and numbers also have the same slant.

Timed Writing

On Monday, Jason's teacher gave the class some assignments for the rest of the week. It was almost time for the bell to ring. Jason had to write quickly. Read the assignments his teacher gave.

> "On Tuesday there will be a spelling test on all the words in Chapter 6. On Wednesday hand in your book reports. Dr. Loman from the Nature Trail Museum will be here Thursday. Please prepare two questions to ask her. Review Unit Three for our social studies test on Friday."

When you have to write quickly, use these tips.
- Listen carefully for the information.
- Use manuscript or cursive, whichever you write faster.
- Skip words that are not important.

Take notes on Jason's assignments in the space below. Time your writing. Use a clock, a timer, or have a partner time you. Stop when four minutes are up.

_____

_____

_____

_____

_____

_____

_____

Read over what you have written. Do you understand the assignments? Did you include only important words?

Reading and Writing

The Long Winter by Laura Ingalls Wilder is about life in pioneer days when the Midwest was being settled. In one chapter, "An Errand to Town," Laura and her little sister Carrie are lost in the tall grass. They are trying to find their father, who is mowing hay.

Read the paragraphs below. They tell how tired and afraid the girls are.

Carrie's mouth opened a little. Her big eyes looked up at Laura and they said, "I know. We're lost." Her mouth shut without a word. If they were lost, they were lost. There was nothing to say about it.

"We'd better go on," Laura said.

"I guess so. As long as we can," Carrie agreed.

They went on. They must surely have passed the place where Pa was mowing. But Laura could not be sure of anything. Perhaps if they thought they turned back, they would really be getting farther away. They could only go on. Now and then they stopped and wiped their sweating faces. They were terribly thirsty but there was no water. They were very tired from pushing through the grasses. Not one single push seemed hard, but going on was harder than trampling hay. Carrie's thin little face was gray-white, she was so tired.

Then Laura thought the grasses ahead were thinner. The shade seemed lighter there and the tops of the grasses against the sky seemed fewer. And suddenly she saw sunshine, yellow beyond the dark grass stems. Perhaps there was a pond there. Oh! perhaps, perhaps there was Pa's stubble field and the mowing machine and Pa.

Have you ever been lost? Where did it happen? How did you feel? Brainstorm to think of some words and phrases that would help you tell a story about being lost and how you felt about it. It might be your own experience. You might prefer to imagine a story about someone else being lost. Write a list of words and phrases below.

_____   _____

_____   _____

_____   _____

_____   _____

Mariza made up a story about two lost children in a park. Read her sentences.

> Kali and Ann were at a picnic with their families. Then they wandered away. They wanted to find rabbits in the woods. Before long, they were completely lost! What could they do? They felt sad and worried.

Read what Mariza wrote.   Yes   No
- Did she use good verbs to tell how the girls became lost?   ☐   ☐
- Did she tell about their feelings?   ☐   ☐

Proofread Mariza's sentences.
- Are all the letters slanted in the same direction? ☐   ☐
- Are the punctuation marks slanted in the same direction as the letters?   ☐   ☐

Copy Mariza's sentences on a sheet of paper. Be sure to slant the letters in the same direction. Slant punctuation marks in the same direction as the letters.

58

Now it's your turn to write about an experience of being lost. Tell what being lost feels like. You may want to use some of the words and phrases from your list.

_____

_____

_____

_____

_____

_____

_____

_____

_____

_____

_____

_____

_____

Read your draft carefully.   Yes   No
- Did you write about the experience of being lost?   ☐   ☐
- Did you tell how the lost person or persons felt?   ☐   ☐

Proofread your writing.
- Are your letters slanted in the same direction?   ☐   ☐
- Are your punctuation marks slanted in the same direction
  as the letters?   ☐   ☐

Edit your copy. Can you think of anything to add to your draft? Make it interesting by including more feelings about being lost. Then copy your revised draft on another sheet of paper.

Fun with Handwriting: Place Cards

Once a year, Mrs. Harlson's fifth-grade class celebrates a day called Everybody's Birthday. Jill and a birthday committee wrote place cards and decorated them for each student's desk. They used nicknames, descriptive words, and funny titles.

Sometimes they used just a first name and sometimes both names. Here are some examples: Prince Henry, Luisa Taylor the Best, Awesome Roy, Classical Addie West.

Read the cards below.

Copy the cards above, or write two other names. Use nicknames and exaggeration. Be creative! Write in either cursive or manuscript.

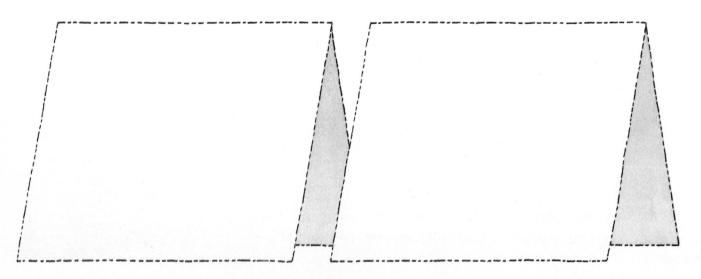

If you want to make an actual place card, use an unlined index card. First fold the card in half. Write the name on both sides. Then stand the card up.

Unit Three
Applying Handwriting Skills

Writing the Time

What time is it? You can write the time shown on the watch in three different ways—half-past two, two-thirty, and 2:30.

When you write the time in numbers, use a colon [:] to separate the hours from the minutes. Write the times below. Be sure to slant your numbers and colons in one direction.

7:35   5:20   8:40

6:03   12:15   9:00

Read the sentences below. Write <u>only</u> the time in each sentence, using numbers and colons. A colon is half as tall as a number. To show the time before noon, use the abbreviation **a.m.** Use the abbreviation **p.m.** to show time later than noon. Write the abbreviations in either manuscript or cursive. Slant your numbers and colons the same way you slant your letters.

Mrs. Day arrives at eight-twenty each morning.

The Clock Shop opens for business at nine.

The mail comes at two-ten in the afternoon.

At four-fifty, Mrs. Day gets ready to leave her job.

Writing a Schedule

Last Friday was a holiday. Rick wrote his schedule for the day. Copy it in cursive. Write small enough to include the times and activities on one line as Rick did. Be sure to make colons half the size of your numbers and tall letters.

8:30 a.m. Ride to the park.
10:10 a.m. Meet Al at the pool.
12:15 p.m. Have a picnic lunch.
1:40 p.m. Go to the library.
4:00 p.m. Return home.
4:50 p.m. Set the table.
6:45 p.m. Help with the dishes.
7:15 p.m. Finish reading Zeely.

Write two times and activities for your own holiday.

Writing Addresses

Ralph wrote a letter to his cousin. Below is the address he wrote on the envelope.

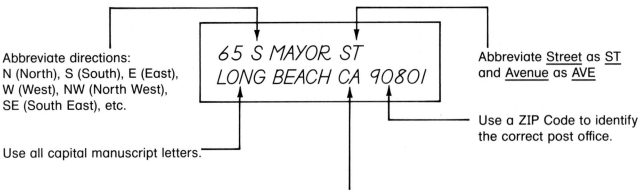

Abbreviate directions:
N (North), S (South), E (East), W (West), NW (North West), SE (South East), etc.

Use all capital manuscript letters.

Abbreviate <u>Street</u> as <u>ST</u> and <u>Avenue</u> as <u>AVE</u>

Use a ZIP Code to identify the correct post office.

Use the Postal Service abbreviations for the states, with no comma between the city and the state.

Copy each address below in manuscript. Be sure to use all capital letters and no punctuation.

405 W HIGH ST
HONOLULU HI 96816

8 SE LINN AVE
ASHLEY AR 72205

2001 BRYAN ST
DALLAS TX 75260

67 S LIND AVE
DYER TN 38134

1 CROWN AVE
BETTENDORF IA 52722

Use the chart above to write your address correctly.

Keeping an Address Book

You might find it easier to use manuscript when you have to write in a small space such as an address book. Look at the listings below.

Name _Takata, Kevin_

Street _305 Heatherton Dr._

City _Fort Wayne_   State _IN_   ZIP _46815_

Telephone _(219) 555-3962_

Name _Thomas, Ann_

Street _640 Adriatic Ave._

City _Atlantic City_   State _NJ_   ZIP _08401_

Telephone _(609) 555-7842_

Now copy one of the listings above on the form below. Write neatly in manuscript. Be sure to adjust your writing to fit the spaces provided.

On the second form below, add your own information in manuscript.

Name

Street

City   State   ZIP

Telephone

Name

Street

City   State   ZIP

Telephone

Writing Measurements

People often use abbreviations when they write measurements. Below is a chart of common abbreviations for measurements. Each has only one or two letters except **gal.** The abbreviation for *inch* is the only one that ends with a period.

inch	**in.**	ounce	**oz**	cup	**c**
foot	**ft**	pound	**lb**	pint	**pt**
millimeter	**mm**	ton	**T**	quart	**qt**
centimeter	**cm**	gram	**g**	gallon	**gal**
meter	**m**	kilogram	**kg**	milliliter	**mL**
kilometer	**km**	metric ton	**t**	liter	**L**

Use the same abbreviation for singular and plural measurements.

Copy the list of items below. Notice that some of the measurements have fractions. Be careful to make the top number in a fraction touch the top line and the bottom number touch the bottom line. Write in cursive.

½ gal white paint _____

I L can floor wax _____

5¾ lb bag grass seed _____

3 ft bookshelves _____

Rewrite the measurements below in cursive. Use abbreviations for the words.

6 millimeters _____   **3 metric tons** _____

5⅔ kilograms _____   **7 tons** _____

4 milliliters _____   **2¼ centimeters** _____

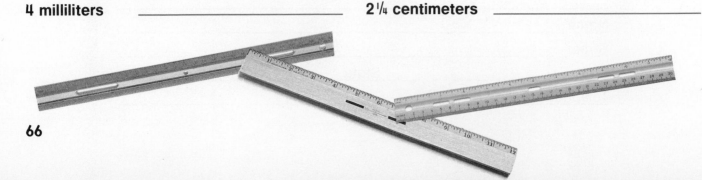

Below is a list of items and their measurements. Rewrite only the measurements in cursive, using numbers and abbreviations. Use the chart on page 66 to help you. Use the same abbreviation for both singular and plural measurements.

baseball bat	**one meter**	
extension cord	**three feet**	
Lake Erie	**ninety-two kilometers**	
dollar bill	**six and one-half centimeters**	
poster	**twenty-eight inches**	
paper clip	**one and one-half inches**	
tennis ball	**two ounces**	
elephant	**five and one-fourth tons**	
ten apples	**three pounds**	
watermelon	**six kilograms**	
four bananas	**one kilogram**	
strawberry	**fifteen kilograms**	
telephone	**three and two-thirds pounds**	
water	**ninety-five milliliters**	
milk	**four quarts**	
tomato juice	**eight pints**	
ice cream	**seven gallons**	
yogurt	**nine liters**	
soup	**five cups**	
maple syrup	**one-half cup**	

Writing Ordinal Numbers

Ordinal numbers show order in a series. They can be written as words or as numbers and letters combined. Look at the chart. Notice that the numbers are not joined to the letters in the second column.

The ribbons show names and positions of some prizewinners in a contest. Write the position of each winner in two ways. Be sure to join letters in the words. Do not join the numbers to the letters.

first	*1st*
second	*2nd*
third	*3rd*
fourth	*4th*
fifth	*5th*
sixth	*6th*
seventh	*7th*
eighth	*8th*
ninth	*9th*
tenth	*10th*

Chris

_____ _____

_____ _____

Rita

_____ _____

_____ _____

Zach

_____ _____

_____ _____

Mary

_____ _____

_____ _____

Kiku

_____ _____

_____ _____

Sara

_____ _____

_____ _____

Tim

_____ _____

_____ _____

Peter

_____ _____

_____ _____

Fran

_____ _____

_____ _____

Lana

_____ _____

_____ _____

Copy the sentences below in cursive. Write the ordinal numbers as numbers and letters combined. Remember not to join numbers to letters, but join the letters.

Marta and I were fifth in line.

_____

_____

We sat in the fourth row.

_____

_____

We could see well from the seventh and eighth seats.

_____

_____

This was the sixth race.

_____

_____

The first judge blew a whistle.

_____

_____

The second official fired the starting gun.

_____

_____

The tenth runner started gaining.

_____

_____

Then the ninth began to pull ahead.

_____

_____

Marta's sister came in third.

_____

_____

Fun with Handwriting: *Calligraphy*

The word *calligraphy* means beautiful handwriting. This art developed in China and then in Europe hundreds of years ago. People still write calligraphy today to decorate greeting cards, signs, and invitations. You can have fun trying it yourself.

Calligraphy is written with a special pen. The nib, or end, is not pointed, but square, like the one in the picture at the right.

This kind of pen produces thick and thin strokes when you hold it at the same angle. Here are some examples of strokes.

Read the paragraphs below. Then copy the instructions in the second paragraph. Write in either manuscript or cursive.

Would you like to practice some calligraphy? A felt-tip marker is excellent for this, because it has a square nib. The next paragraph gives instructions to help you write calligraphy.

Use paper with widely spaced lines. Hold the pen at a 45-degree angle. Keep this same position as you change from one stroke to another. You will make both thick and thin strokes naturally. Do not put pressure on your marker. Keep your touch light and even.

_____

_____

_____

_____

_____

_____

_____

_____

_____

_____

_____

_____

_____

There are many good books about learning calligraphy. You can also see examples of it on greeting cards, invitations, and announcements. Sometimes advertisements are written in calligraphy. Look around and notice how often this beautiful handwriting is used.

Fun with Handwriting: Membership Cards

Below is a membership card that Randy created for his club. He invited everyone in his class to join. Notice that the club rules are at the bottom of the card.

Official Member
The Happiness Club

Name __Randy Dunbar__

Street Address __315 E. 16th St.__

City, State, ZIP __Dubuque IA 52001__

RULES
I promise to make up jokes and riddles once a week, to laugh with my friends twice a week, and to smile at everyone every day.

Signature __Randy Dunbar__

Make a membership card for your own club in the space below. You might like to talk over the club with some of your friends. Give it a name, and make up some rules. Write in manuscript. Remember to sign your name in cursive.

Letter, Word, and Sentence Spacing

You can make your handwriting legible by spacing letters evenly. Write the words below.

growing

changing

Can you read the sentence below?

Spacingisanimportantpartoflegibility.

The sentence is **Spacing is an important part of legibility.**
Why is it hard to read?

Write the sentence legibly on the lines below. Be sure to space your letters evenly. Leave more space between words than between letters in words.

Copy the paragraph in cursive. As you write, concentrate on spacing. You should allow more space between sentences than between words in a sentence.

Jean Little writes award-winning books for children. She is partially blind, but travels extensively with the help of her guide dog, Zephyr.

Below is the first part of a poem by Jean Little. It is taken from her book, *Hey World, Here I Am!*

About Notebooks

I love the first page of a new notebook.
I write the date crisply.
My whole name marches exactly along the line.
The spaces are always even.
The commas curl just so.
I never have to erase on the first page.
Never!

When I get to the middle, there are lots of eraser holes.
The corners are dog-eared.
Whole paragraphs have been crossed out.
My words slide off the lines and crowd together.
I wish it was done . . . .

Copy the poem. Adjust your handwriting to fit each line of the poem on one writing line.

Timed Writing

Tirella listened carefully and wrote notes when her volleyball coach made an important announcement over the public address system at school. Read the announcement below.

"**Next Thursday, October 14, we will play Lincoln School in their gym. Now please listen. This is a change from the schedule you received last week. Game time is 4:00 p.m. If you need a ride, call Mr. Nelson at 386-4714 between 10:00 a.m. and 2:00 p.m. You must call *before* Wednesday, October 13. Lincoln School is at 9006 Court Avenue. The entrance to the gym is on the west side of the building. Please be there by 3:15.**"

Sometimes you need to write rapidly while listening to someone. When you do, use these tips.
- Listen carefully.
- Use manuscript or cursive, whichever you write faster.
- Skip unimportant words and phrases.

Take notes from the announcement in the space below. Time your writing. Use a clock, a timer, or ask someone to time you. Stop writing when four minutes are up.

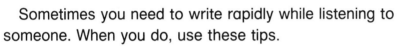

Read your notes on the announcement. Did you include all important information and leave out the rest? Is your writing legible?

Writing a Get-Well Message

When John's grandfather was in the hospital, John decorated a card and wrote a get-well message for him. Read John's message.

December 20, 199_

Dear Grandpa,

    We had too much homework last night. Sue helped me with some of it.

    I heard a joke in school today. How do you stop a mouse from squeaking? Oil it. I like your jokes better. Please get well and come home soon.

        With love,

        John

Copy John's get-well message, or write one of your own in the space below. Write in manuscript. Remember to slant all your letters in the same direction. Try to keep your writing straight even though there are no lines.

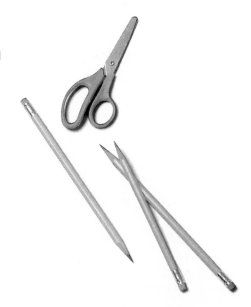

Writing Punctuation Marks

Notice the position of the punctuation marks below.
Quotation marks are in pairs, facing each other. Copy each
mark carefully.

.	?	!	'	,	" "
period	question mark	exclamation mark	apostrophe	comma	quotation marks

When you write contractions in cursive, do not join the
letters on either side of the apostrophe. Copy the words
below.

can't   *here's*   *I'll*

Copy each sentence in cursive. Remember to slant all
punctuation marks in the same direction as your letters.

Have you ever learned sign language?

Jan's friend taught it to her.

How helpful he was!

Jan said, "This is really hard, but I like it."

Now make up a sentence of your own. Try to use four of
the punctuation marks above. Write the sentence in cursive.

Writing a Journal Entry

Even when you write only for yourself, your writing should be legible. Notice how neatly Rosa wrote this entry in her journal. It will be easy for her to read later.

*July 29, 199_*

I felt both happy and sad today. I was sad because my best friend Tina left for camp this morning. She will be gone for two weeks, and I will miss her very much. We promised to write each other. I was very excited this afternoon when Dad took me to the warehouse where he works. He showed me the computer he uses to do his job. I had a great time!

Think of something you would like to write about in a journal entry. Write some words and phrases on the lines below. Here are some suggestions to get you started.

missing a friend	sharing a good time	sadness
finding something I had lost	needing help	excitement
improving my swimming	the best sport	being proud

Now write your own journal entry. Begin with the date. Write about something that you won't mind sharing with others. Use the ideas you wrote on page 78 or some other ideas. Be sure to write neatly in cursive. Make all your letters slant in the same direction.

Writing Titles and Abbreviations

Like proper nouns, titles also begin with capital letters. Look at the titles and their abbreviations below.

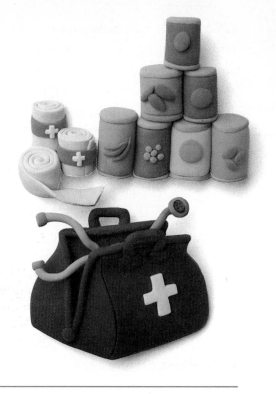

Captain	Senator	Major	Doctor
Capt.	**Sen.**	**Maj.**	**Dr.**

The sentences below tell about important people in the life of Clara Barton, founder of the American Red Cross. Write the sentences in cursive. Use abbreviations for the titles. Remember that some capital letters are joined to the lower-case letters that follow them, and some are not joined.

Captain Stephen Barton, Clara's father, taught her to be kind to others.

_____

_____

_____

Clara got help from Senator Henry Wilson in providing food and care for wounded soldiers.

_____

_____

_____

Doctor Clarence Cutter set up a hospital.

_____

_____

Major D.H. Rucker provided supplies, a warehouse, and an ambulance.

_____

_____

Doctor James I. Dunn worked for hours without sleep to help the wounded.

_____

_____

_____

Look at the proper nouns and titles you wrote. Do your capital letters touch the top line? Did you join capital letters correctly?

Writing Proper Nouns

Sam wrote the paragraph below about the American Red Cross. He forgot to capitalize most of the proper nouns. Rewrite the paragraph in cursive. Remember that capital letters always touch the top line. Some capital letters also have descenders. Be sure to keep your tall letters from bumping into letters with descenders when you write.

We saw a movie today about clara barton. She founded the american Red Cross, which helps victims of disasters. She nursed soldiers during the Civil War. Later she went to switzerland, france, germany, and Russia. Many people helped her. The red cross aided people in the united states. There were floods on the ohio river and a forest fire in michigan. In peace and war, the red cross works to help others.

Writing Dates

The chart below shows months and days with their abbreviations. They all begin with capital letters. Notice that May, June, and July are not abbreviated, because they have no more than four letters.

Months	January	February	March	April	May	June
	Jan.	**Feb.**	**Mar.**	**Apr.**	**May**	**June**
	July	August	September	October	November	December
	July	**Aug.**	**Sept.**	**Oct.**	**Nov.**	**Dec.**

Days	Sunday	Monday	Tuesday	Wednesday	Thursday	Friday	Saturday
	Sun.	**Mon.**	**Tues.**	**Wed.**	**Thurs.**	**Fri.**	**Sat.**

Copy the dates below. Remember to write a comma between the day and the year. In dates where the day of the week comes first, write a comma between the day and the month. Write periods after abbreviations.

September 1, 1939

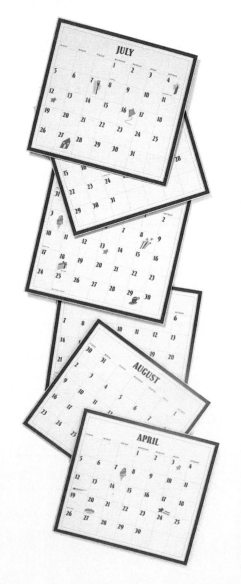

Dec. 16, 1897

Nov. 21, 1973

June 12, 1923

January 31, 1985

Sunday, Feb. 25

Tuesday, April 19

82

Keeping a Birthday List

It's fun to make a list of the birthdays of your friends and relatives. They will be surprised when you remember their dates. Read part of Winston's list below.

DaSean Hillsman   Apr. 4, 1979

Aunt Kate   Jan. 22, 1965

Write a list of names of people whose birthdays you want to remember. Next to each name, write the date. Be sure to make small letters half as tall as capital letters. Use abbreviations for the months that have abbreviations.

Timed Writing

Rosita asked for directions on how to get to Mia's house. Below are the directions Mia gave. Rosita wrote them rapidly.

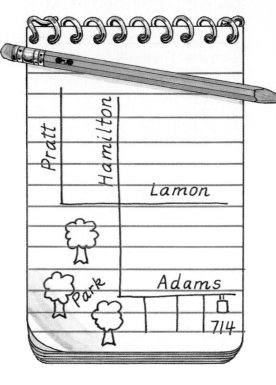

"Go south on Pratt to Lamon. Then turn left on Lamon to Hamilton. Turn right. Go one block to Adams. Turn left and go three blocks to my house, 714 Adams. It's gray brick on the right side of the street."

If you need to write directions on how to get somewhere, use these tips.
- Write manuscript or cursive, whichever is faster for you.
- Write only important words.
- Be sure you understand the directions.

Write Mia's directions in the space below. Time your writing. Use a clock, a timer, or ask someone to time you. Stop writing when three minutes are up.

_____

_____

_____

_____

_____

_____

_____

Now read what you wrote. Do you understand the directions? Did you include only important words?

Fun with Handwriting: Riddles

   All the riddles below are about letters of the alphabet. The answers are at the bottom of the page. Find each answer and write it under the riddle. Write in cursive or manuscript.

Why does Lucy like the letter K?

_____

_____

What makes a road broad?

_____

_____

What's in the church?
But not in the steeple?
The parson has it,
But not the people.

_____

_____

How do you make the word "one" disappear?

_____

_____

What do you have in December that you don't have in any other month?

_____

_____

ANSWERS

Put a G at the beginning and it's "gone."
The letter D.   The letter R.
It makes Lucy lucky.   The letter B.

Writing Titles

In writing, titles are marked in a special way. If the title is a book, underline it. If it is a poem, put quotation marks around it. In all titles, capitalize the first, last, and all important words. Quotation marks should slant the same way as your letters. Look at the examples below.

The Pinballs is a book that tells about three children who meet in a foster home.

The best poem I read this year is "Harriet Tubman."

Copy the paragraphs below in cursive. Be sure to rewrite titles correctly.

I like to read books and poems about friends and families. In the book The Day Chubby Became Charles, Julia learns that Charles cares about her. She tells him about her sick grandmother. He is a good listener.

Arnold Adoff wrote a book called Eats. It has funny poems. The poem I like best is I Am Learning.

Writing a List of Books and Poems

   Write the titles of your favorite books or poems.
Remember to underline the titles of books and put quotation
marks around the titles of poems. Space letters evenly and
leave even more space between words.

Writing a Poem

The poem below is lined up straight on the left side. Each line begins with a capital letter, whether or not it begins a sentence. Many poems are written this way.

The Falling Star

I saw a star slide down the sky,
Blinding the north as it went by,
Too burning and too quick to hold,
Too lovely to be bought or sold,
Good only to make wishes on
And then forever to be gone.

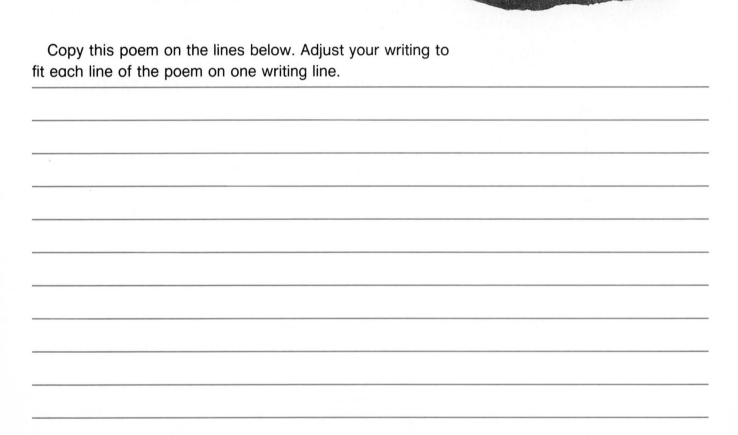

Sara Teasdale

Copy this poem on the lines below. Adjust your writing to fit each line of the poem on one writing line.

Here is another poem.

On the Beach

The sun draws
Lines of fire
Along my legs as I lie
Stretched out as far as I can reach
Face downwards on the beach.

Finding the exact middle spot of my back
The sun warms this too
Till all of a sudden
Like a big blue wet washrag
A breeze off the sea hits me all over: smack.

Dorothy Aldis

Copy the poem below, or try writing a poem of your own.
You might want it to have rhyming words or no rhymes at all.

_____

_____

_____

_____

_____

_____

_____

_____

_____

_____

Making a Sign

Sometimes you need to change your handwriting to fit a large space. Your writing is larger, but the letters should keep the correct size and proportion.

Practice writing the words below in manuscript. Write in a large size. Notice that the words have small, tall, capital, and descender letters.

Age   Fly   Sit

Rod Wax Truck

Willy's school was having a talent show. He made a sign for the bulletin board. Notice that all the letters in his last line are capitals.

Copy the words on Willy's sign, or make your own. Write large in manuscript.

**What's your talent?
Enter the show.
SIGN UP TODAY!**

Writing a Business Letter

Read Max's business letter. Notice that it follows a pattern. It has six parts. Then copy the letter in cursive below. Use adult proportion. Concentrate on your joining strokes. Remember that only capital letters that end at the bottom line are joined to the letters that follow them. Be sure to join all lower-case letters.

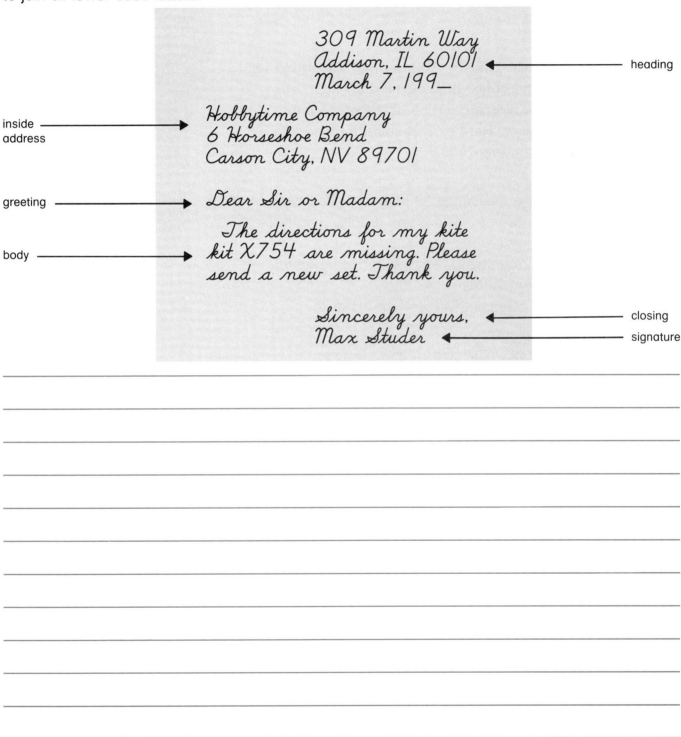

309 Martin Way
Addison, IL 60101 ← heading
March 7, 199_

inside → Hobbytime Company
address   6 Horseshoe Bend
            Carson City, NV 89701

greeting → Dear Sir or Madam:

body →   The directions for my kite
           kit X754 are missing. Please
           send a new set. Thank you.

                    Sincerely yours, ← closing
                    Max Studer ← signature

Timed Writing

Koyi took two telephone messages for her mother. She had to write very fast. At the same time, her writing had to be legible. Read the messages below.

"Hello. This is Myra Durk. Please tell your mother to call me at work as soon as possible. The number is 423–8758. Thank you."

"Hi. This is Jim Zilinsky. Your mother asked me to send her the insurance papers. I'll drop them off early tomorrow morning. I'll be at the office until about 6:30 tonight. Here's my number in case she doesn't have it—698-2400."

You often take phone messages for someone. You need to listen carefully and write both quickly and legibly. Use these tips.

- Use manuscript or cursive, whichever you write faster.
- Write only important words.
- If you aren't sure of something, ask the caller to repeat it.

Take the important information from the telephone messages in the space below. Time your writing. Use a clock, a timer, or have someone time you. Stop writing when four minutes are up.

_____

_____

_____

_____

_____

_____

_____

Read the messages you wrote. Is the information clear? Did you write only important words?

Reading and Writing

"About Black Cowboys" is a chapter in the book *Justin and the Best Biscuits in the World* by Mildred Pitts Walter. It is a story about a boy visiting his grandfather's ranch.

One day his grandfather tells Justin about some famous black cowboys. One was Bill Pickett, who created the rodeo sport of bulldogging—grabbing the horns of a steer and throwing it to the ground.

Read what Justin's grandfather tells about other black cowboys.

"One cowboy named Williams taught Rough Rider Teddy Roosevelt how to break horses; and another one named Clay taught Will Rogers, the comedian, the art of roping." Grandpa offered Justin the last biscuit.

When they had finished their lunch they led the horses away from the shed to graze. As they watched the horses, Grandpa went on, "Now, there were some more very famous black cowboys. Jessie Stahl. They say he was the best rider of wild horses in the West."

"How could he be? Nobody ever heard about him. I didn't."

"Oh, there're lots of famous blacks you never hear or read about. You ever hear about Deadwood Dick?"

Justin laughed. "No."

"There's another one. His real name was Nate Love. He could outride, outshoot anyone. In Deadwood City in the Dakota Territory, he roped, tied, saddled, mounted, and rode a wild horse faster than anyone. Then in the shooting match, he hit the bull's-eye every time. The people named him Deadwood Dick right on the spot. Enough about cowboys, now. While the horses graze, let's clean up here and get back to our men's work."

Who are some famous people you have heard of? What do you know about them? They may be well known throughout the country or just in the town where you live. Make a list in the Word Bank of words that will help you tell something about one famous person and why he or she is famous.

Word Bank

_____   _____

_____   _____

_____   _____

_____   _____

Beth likes running and jumping. She read about Jackie Joyner-Kersee and decided to write about her. Read her opening sentences.

> *Jackie Joyner-Kersee is famous for setting records in heptathlon. She once jumped 24 feet, 5 ½ inches. In Moscow she ran 200 meters in 23 seconds. She was named the best athlete in the United States in 1986.*

Read what Beth wrote.
                                            Yes   No
- Did she write about a famous person?   ☐   ☐
- Did she tell why that person is famous?   ☐   ☐

Proofread Beth's sentences.
- Are her letters evenly spaced?   ☐   ☐
- Does she have spacing between words and even more between sentences?   ☐   ☐

Copy Beth's sentences on a sheet of paper. Be sure to space letters evenly. Leave space between words and even more between sentences.

Now write about a famous person you have heard or read about. Tell why the person is famous. You may want to use some words from your Word Bank.

_____

_____

_____

_____

_____

_____

_____

_____

_____

_____

_____

Read your draft carefully.
- Did you write about a famous person?
- Did you tell why she or he is famous?

Yes ☐ No ☐
Yes ☐ No ☐

Proofread your work.
- Are your letters evenly spaced?
- Do you have spacing between words and even more between sentences?

☐ ☐

☐ ☐

Think of some changes that will improve your composition. Add more information about the famous person you are writing about. Then write the revised copy on another sheet of paper.

Index